YOU CRACK THE CASE

CITY OF TERROR

STEVE BARLOW & STEVE SKIDMORE

ILLUSTRATED BY DAVID COUSENS

LONDON·SYDNEY

First published in 2011
by Franklin Watts

Text © Steve Barlow and Steve Skidmore 2011
Illustrations by David Cousens © Franklin Watts 2011
"The 2 Steves" logo used with kind permission of Orchard Books
Cover design by Peter Scoulding

Franklin Watts
338 Euston Road
London NW1 3BH

Franklin Watts Australia
Level 17/207 Kent Street
Sydney, NSW 2000

A CIP catalogue record for this book
is available from the British Library.

ISBN: 978 0 7496 9286 5

1 3 5 7 9 10 8 6 4 2

Printed in Great Britain

Franklin Watts is a division of Hachette Children's Books,
an Hachette UK company.
www.hachette.co.uk

An adventure where YOU crack the case!

This book is not like others you may have read. In this story YOU have to make decisions to solve the crime. Each section of this book is numbered. At the end of each section, YOU will have to make a choice. The choice YOU make will lead to a different section of the book.

Some choices will be correct, others will not. You must make the right choices by looking at the evidence, solving puzzles or even breaking codes. Make sure that you LOOK carefully at the pictures – they *could* give you vital clues.

If you make a bad decision you may receive a warning from your boss, or get thrown off the case. Some of your decisions could even be fatal!

Record how many BAD DECISIONS and WARNINGS you get from your boss. When you have cracked the case – or been kicked off it – you'll get a Crime Team Agent Rating that will show how well – or how badly – you've done.

You are the leader of Crime Team, a section of the International Police Federation based in New York City, USA. You are one of the world's leading experts in cracking cases that no one else can. You have solved crimes across the globe and have made many enemies, who would like to see you dead…

YOUR MISSION

» To aid and support national police forces anywhere in the world.
» To tackle the toughest cases and solve mysteries that others cannot.

YOUR TEAM

Your team contains the best of the best – top investigative experts from around the world.
You will have to make decisions about how to use your team and whose skills will be best suited to help solve the crime.

YOUR BOSS
COMMANDER TUCKER

Ex-military, ex-New York Police Department, ex-CIA and currently your bad-ass boss. Given half a chance, Commander Tucker will chew your butt. He will alert you to BAD DECISIONS and give you WARNINGS. He might even THROW YOU OFF the case!

YOUR SIDEKICK
LEON PEREZ

JOB: Your constant sidekick and legman – Leon does all the stuff you're too busy to do yourself and is also the "muscle".

EXPERTISE: A ballistics expert with a wide knowledge of all types of weapon.

NOTES: It is said he can smell a bullet and tell you which gun it came from – he's that good!

DOCTOR ANUSHA DAS

JOB: Forensic pathologist

EXPERTISE: Brilliant at establishing the time and cause of death of a victim.

NOTES: Extensive knowledge of poisons and diseases.

SUN LIN

JOB: Forensic scientist

EXPERTISE: An expert at fingerprinting, DNA analysis and other forensic techniques.

NOTES: Has the ability to remember everything she has seen or heard. Never forgets a face, remembers every crime report and excellent at finding all kinds of information.

DARIUS KING ("BUGS")

JOB: Computer expert
EXPERTISE: A genius at hacking, data retrieval and electronic surveillance.
NOTES: Is an expert in using computers to help with HID (Human Identification at a Distance) to identify suspects and criminals.

TODD BLACKWOOD

JOB: Profiler (forensic psychologist)
EXPERTISE: Can "get inside" the minds of criminals and predict what they will do next.
NOTES: Also an expert in espionage, counter-espionage and terrorism.

» NOW GO TO SECTION 1.

1

You are on the trail of an international mercenary! He will work for any government or group that pays him. He is ruthless – once he has taken a job, he never breaks a contract, no matter what. His true identity is unknown, but to those who deal with him he is called "The Cobra". You have come across him before, in fact you are one of very few people to have actually met him and survived!

You are sitting in a café on Guernsey, one of the Channel Islands, situated off the coast of France.

Leon Perez, your sidekick, has flown in from New York to meet you. He crashes down in the chair opposite and you order him a strong coffee.

"Commander Tucker says 'hi' and wants to know why you haven't found The Cobra yet?" says Leon. He looks around. "And why have I had to fly here? I thought you were in South America."

You grunt. "It's become more complicated," you reply. "I've arranged to meet an agent from British intelligence tonight. He has information about The Cobra."

"Tell me more," says Perez.

» **If you want to tell Perez about the case, go to 42.**

» **If you want to head out and meet the British spy, go to 34.**

2

"I think we should head over to the Bank of England and stake it out," you say. "If The Cobra turns up, I'll be able to identify him from my meeting with him and we can grab him."

There is an embarrassed silence in the room before Tucker's voice rings out. "That is darn stupid on so many levels! How long are you going to have to wait before he shows up? How are you going to stake out all the area around the bank – personally? And how will you even recognise him? He'd be stupid if he didn't put on a disguise. Most importantly, you don't know for certain that the bank is the target!"

Tucker went on. "If you don't start thinking clearly, I'll take you off the case. You're showing up me and the Crime Team in front of these stuck-up Brits – no offence, Sir James. Consider this a warning! You need to follow the target from his last known position!"

» **YOU'VE RECEIVED A WARNING FROM TUCKER!**
Make a note of this and go to 14.

3

You call Sir James and tell him Cobra's location.

Within minutes armed Secret Service agents arrive and quickly surrounded The Cobra. He pulls out a gun. It is a fatal mistake. He is shot down in a hail of bullets.

As The Cobra's lifeless body is taken away, Sir James arrives and thanks you. "A good job, well done."

"Maybe," you murmur. "But where is the bomb?"

Four hours later you find out. As you wait in the airport departure lounge, news reports come in of an explosion in central London. Many people have been killed and radioactivity is spreading through the city.

Your phone rings. It is Tucker. "You fool," he cries, "The Cobra had stashed the bomb in a left luggage office. He'd already set it, so it went off when he didn't arrive to collect it. You should have found it! You made a bad decision. Get back here and clear out your desk. I can't have someone like you running my team."

» **YOU'VE BEEN THROWN OFF THE TEAM!**
To see how you rate as a detective, go to 46.

4

"We can manage on our own," you tell Perez. He raises an eyebrow at this decision.

Peters shakes his head. "I spoke to your boss, Commander Tucker, and explained that we need as much help as we can get. He said to let him know which team members you need."

Perez smiles at you. "Don't worry, I won't tell Tucker that you wanted all the glory just for you and me!"

» **YOU MADE A BAD DECISION, *BUT GOT AWAY WITH IT!***

Go to 21.

5

You remember what happened to Gomez. You know The Cobra is ruthless and cannot be trusted. You aim your gun.

"Cobra!"

He spins round. He has a gun in his hand, but he is too slow. You pull your trigger and your shot hits him in the chest. He drops to the floor. You rush over to him and kick away his gun.

He looks up. He is bleeding badly and dying.

"Crime Team!" he laughs. "You are too late again! You may have killed me, but the bomb is activated and will still go off in a few minutes.

The barrier will be destroyed and the Thames will flood, causing devastation to London. You will never guess the code to stop the countdown…" With those last taunting words, he dies.

You rush over to the case. The countdown display tells you that you have less than a minute to deactivate the bomb.

You realise that to stop it exploding, you must type in the correct code. Desperately you try to think where you might have seen a code with seven letters or numbers…

Suddenly you have an idea. You have heard a code – the postcode that Agent Smith mentioned and Perez worked out. You thought it was the bomb's target – what if it was really the code to deactivate the bomb? But what was the code?

» **If you think it was EC8R 2AH, go to 31.**
» **If you think it was EC2R 8AH, go to 36.**

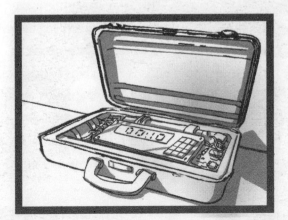

6

You look at Perez and shake your head. "Maybe you've heard it in your dreams, Leon…"

Sir James raises an eyebrow. "I must say, I'm interested in what your man has to contribute. Let him speak up, there's a good chap."

You realise that Sir James is too polite to criticise your handling of your own team, but he thinks you'd be a fool to ignore Perez's advice. Insulting Perez in front of the MI5 agents has made you look like a bad leader.

"Sorry, Leon," you apologise. "What are you thinking?"

"Say Smith's last words again," says Perez.

» **YOU MADE A BAD DECISION.**
   Make a note of it and go to 32.

7

You look at the screen. "He isn't carrying a bag, so the bomb could be anywhere," you tell Perez and Todd. "We have to follow him. He'll be passing through the lobby in a minute or two. Todd, Bugs has a Bluetooth device that'll allow him to hack into The Cobra's phone and steal information about recent calls and contacts. It only has a short range, so tell him to activate it as soon as The Cobra appears."

"Will do," replies Todd. He heads out into the lobby.

You and Perez take up positions near the reception desk, where you can see what happens. The lift doors open and The Cobra walks out. He is still holding his phone. You see Bugs tap at the keys of his laptop as The Cobra passes by him. Bugs looks over at you and nods.

The Cobra heads out of the hotel. What should you do now? You have to make a quick decision!

» **If you want to call in MI5, go to 3.**
» **If you want all the team to follow The Cobra, go to 30.**
» **If you decide that you and Perez should follow him, go to 17.**

8

You nod. "Yes, we're Crime Team."

The man shows you his ID. "Peters, Special Branch Officer. I was supposed to be working with Agent Smith – I believe you knew him."

You look puzzled. "Knew?"

Peters nods. "I'm afraid his body has been found in a hotel room. He'd been stabbed to death. Some hours ago, it seems."

You raise an eyebrow. "Any witnesses or leads?"

"As he was dying, he managed to phone his intelligence bosses in London. He said that The Cobra was responsible. He also said The Cobra had been paid to carry out a major terrorist attack on London. He mentioned the possibility of a nuclear 'dirty' bomb."

You whistle. "That is not good."

"We've put out a search for this Cobra character, but no one knows what he looks like!

We think he may have got off the island. My contacts in London would like you to visit them. After all, you are one of the few people in the world who knows what The Cobra looks like…"

» **If you wish to visit the bank to investigate the money trail, go to 16.**

» **If you think you should head to London, go to 39.**

9

Before you can leave, you hear a beeping noise from Bugs's computer.

"It's The Cobra," says Bugs. "I put a trace onto his phone." He looks at the screen. "He's moving along the River Thames. He must be in a boat!"

You check the map. "He must be heading to the barrier. Let's get going…" You all hurry out of the hotel. The roads are heavy with traffic.

"We'll never make it in time," says Sun Lin. Just then a motorbike pulls up and the rider takes off his helmet. "Yes, we will," you reply. "The rest of you try to get to the barrier fast…"

You rush across to the motorbike rider, push him away, grab the helmet and leap on the bike. "Sorry, sir! Gotta save the city!" You twist the throttle and speed off towards the Thames, swerving and dodging between the cars.

Your heart races as you weave through the traffic. Horns blare at you as you buzz past.

Eventually you reach the north bank of the River Thames. You race along it before you see a group of sea cadets getting out of a high-powered boat. You dump the bike, rush onto the pier, and as the cadets stare at you in astonishment, you rev up the boat's outboard motor and speed away downriver.

You phone Bugs. "Patch my phone into your computer and link me up with The Cobra's position. Where is he?"

Soon Bugs has the answer. "He's about half a mile ahead of you, just a couple of miles from the barrier. You should be on him in minutes. We've alerted MI5 – they're going to bring Special Forces in using helicopters."

» **If you think you should get close enough to take out The Cobra now, go to 27.**

» **If you want to call off Special Forces and continue to follow him, go to 37.**

10

The traffic proves not to be a problem and you soon arrive at Thames House.

"It's an impressive building," you say.

"Must be hundreds of years old," says Perez. The driver shakes her head. "No, not really. It was built after the River Thames flooded in 1928 and destroyed the area. The old properties were pulled down and this was built."

"Thanks for the history lesson," mutters Perez.

"I thought you could do with it," replies the driver.

You pass through the security checks and are taken to the briefing room.

There are several agents sitting at computers and monitors. You are introduced to Sir James Palmer, head of MI5. "Glad you can join us, gentlemen. Given the urgency of the situation let's get straight down to business."

Sir James hands you a document. "This is the transcript of the last communication we had with our agent on Guernsey. We couldn't get the whole message. The poor chap was dying after all…"

>>>>>>>>> TOP SECRET <<<<<<<<<

FINAL SPOKEN COMMUNICATION OF
AGENT SMITH
I'm dying... Cobra [words
unintelligible] stabbed... Attack
planned... [words unintelligible]
Cobra hired... detonate a dirty
bomb... target London [words
unintelligible] within five days...
[following words garbled] easy too
are ate ay a ch—

>>>>>>>>> END OF MESSAGE <<<<<<<<<

"A dirty bomb," you say.

Sir James looks grim. "Yes – a conventional
bomb, but combined with radioactive material."

» **If you want to know more about "dirty"
bombs, go to 18.**
» **If you want to get on with the
investigation, go to 23.**

11

"OK, there's no point staying here," you finally say.
You call Bugs and tell him what has happened.

"I've got something from The Cobra's phone
you might be interested in," says Bugs.

"We're on our way." You and Perez return to

the hotel, where the others are looking at Bugs's laptop computer.

Bugs points at the screen. "There was very little on his phone. It must be a new one, bought especially for this job. There were a couple of calls to a foreign-based number – I'll work on that later – but I got this message from an incoming text. It was encrypted, but it didn't take me long to break it. It's some sort of a code."

A4 C1 B4 O2 A1 A4
A4 B2 C1 B3 A1 R4
O1 C1 B4 B4 R2 A1 B4

You look at the puzzle. "Any ideas?"

Todd speaks up. "There are only five letters. A, C, B, O and R."

You suddenly realise what it means. "They spell COBRA! It must be a substitution grid."

You take a piece of paper and begin scribble on it…

» **Go to 41.**

12

"OK, team. We've done all we can here."

"But, boss…" protests Perez.

You give him a hard stare. He shuts up and you

all head out of Thames House to a local café.

"MI5 is making a big mistake," you say. "It is just jumping in with both feet. I'm still the only one who has met The Cobra and can positively identify him. We have to find him. There's another thing – something in those pictures of the drivers that is nagging at me." You try to think what it was.

"So which hotel do we go to?" asks Sun Lin.

» **If you wish to head to the Empire hotel, go to 24.**

» **If you wish to head to The Ritz hotel, go to 40.**

13

The plane lands at the airport and you are soon inside the terminal.

A young woman meets you and shows you her ID card. "I'm your driver," she says. "Please follow me…"

You make your way to the car park and get into an SUV.

"I'm taking you to Thames House – the HQ of MI5," the driver tells you. She switches on the car's sat nav.

Perez looks surprised. "What sort of driver are you? Don't you know the way?"

"This will give me live traffic updates," she explains. "London traffic can be a nightmare. If I put in the postcode and there's a problem, then it'll calculate another route."

"What's a postcode?" asks Perez.

"It's the British equivalent of a ZIP code in the US," she replies. She taps at the sat nav. "SW1P 1AE. That's the postcode for Thames House."

"The British," sighs Perez, "why can't they use proper English? And the car's steering wheel is on the wrong side."

The driver gives him a hard stare and you laugh at Perez as you head to your meeting with MI5.

» **Go to 10.**

14

"OK," you say, "we have to follow The Cobra's trail from Guernsey. We know he was on the island when he killed Smith. He can't have flown off the island as all flights were cancelled due to the weather. The ferries were also cancelled."

Perez speaks up. "Not all of them. The last ferry left just before the body was discovered."

"Where was it heading?" you ask.

Sir James pulls the information up on screen. "It docked in Portsmouth several hours ago."

You nod. "He must have been on that one. Leon, Sun Lin, check passenger lists and car details. Bugs, you liaise with MI5 and check out all vehicle movements from Portsmouth to London. He's heading here for sure."

"I'll use the Security Service's new 3D vehicle registration plate identification cameras," says Bugs.

The head of MI5 raises an eyebrow. "How did you know about that?"

Bugs winks. "I have my sources…"

You continue. "Todd, I want you to work with me on a profile of what The Cobra looks like and what he may be thinking. OK team, get cracking – we've got to find The Cobra before he detonates the bomb."

» Go to 28.

15

You tell the team about the Thames Barrier and how it is designed to stop London from being destroyed by flooding.

"It's the perfect target for The Cobra," says Todd. "If the control room that operates the barrier was blown up with a dirty bomb, the barrier wouldn't rise and people wouldn't be able to repair it for years. The damage would be colossal."

You nod. "Bugs, check the weather reports and see if the barrier is going to be raised in the near future."

Minutes later he has the information. "High tides, storm weather due – high risk of flooding. The barrier is going to be raised in the next hour."

You look grim. "Todd, ring Sir James and tell him what we've found out. We'll head to the barrier – we have to stop The Cobra detonating the bomb."

» **Go to 9.**

16

"I need to follow the money trail," you tell Peters.

"I was afraid that you might say that." He takes out his phone and taps at the screen. "I'm afraid your man wants to follow the money," he says into the phone.

You hear a stream of bad language as Peters hands you the phone. You know it is your boss, Tucker. Before you can speak he roars down the line. "What the heck are you playin' at? There's a major terrorist incident brewing! You're one of the few people who have seen this Cobra figure and you want to follow some money trail? What sort of clue do you need to be put in front of your eyes? Get your sorry ass over to London, England and think about your actions. If I have to tell you again, I'm taking you off this case! And that's a warning!"

He rings off and, with a sheepish look, you hand the phone back to Peters. Perez is trying hard not to laugh.

» **YOU'VE RECEIVED A WARNING FROM TUCKER!**
Make a note of this and go to 39.

17

You signal to the others to hold back.

"Leon, follow me," you say. You wait for a few seconds to make sure that The Cobra doesn't double back into the lobby, before following him out of the hotel.

You and Perez "double-team" The Cobra, each of you taking it in turns to follow closely before the other one takes over. He makes his way through the busy London streets, but you and Perez keep tabs on him.

Eventually, The Cobra heads towards an Underground station and suddenly breaks into a run. He disappears down the steps.

"Quickly, Leon," you say. You follow him down the steps and curse as a large crowd of people head towards you. You try to force your way through the crowd, but by the time you make your way into the station, The Cobra has disappeared. You look for several minutes, but there are too many people in the station and too many exits to cover.

» **If you want to keep looking for The Cobra, go to 33.**

» **If you want to see if Bugs has picked up any clues, go to 11.**

18

"I know that a dirty bomb contaminates an area with radioactive material," you say to Sir James. "But what would its effects be in London?"

"It depends on its size," replies Sir James. "But if the bomb is being carried by The Cobra, it can't be a big one. It wouldn't blow up a large area, or even cause many deaths through radiation poisoning."

"So why would he use it?" you ask.

"It is designed to create terror in the city. In the area of the explosion, there could be years of cleaning up the radioactive material, making the area totally unusable. It could have a huge economic impact."

"That could be what the people who have hired The Cobra want," you say. "But where would be the best place to cause most damage?"

Sir James shakes his head. "There are so many places. The Stock Exchange or the Houses of Parliament. Major tourist hot spots like the Tower of London or Buckingham Palace…"

"Perhaps that is what Agent Smith was trying to tell us," you say. You pick up the document again.

```
[following words garbled] easy
too are ate ay a ch–
```

"What did he mean?" you wonder.

Sir James shrugs. "We've run them through our computer programs, but come up with nothing… it seems to be gibberish."

You say the words, "E see two r ate ay a ch."

Perez looks at you. "We've heard something like that recently…"

» **If you think you have, go to 32.**

» **If you think Perez is losing the plot, go to 6.**

19

"I think we should tell MI5," you say.

Perez scowls. "Are you sure, boss? They didn't seem to want to know us…"

You pick up your phone but before you can call Sir James, Todd speaks up.

"Boss, you're making a bad call. You don't want MI5 or the police crawling all over The Ritz. The Cobra will soon realise that he's been traced. He could get away or if he has the bomb and is backed into a corner, he could even detonate it. I'm also sure that he'll ditch his female disguise. We need you to help identify him, not MI5."

You realise that Todd is right.

» **YOU MADE A BAD DECISION!**
   Make a note of this and go to 38.

20

You tell the other team members to get ready. You wait by the reception desk. Minutes later, The Cobra appears. As he passes the desk, he looks up and recognises you!

Before you can react he draws a gun and fires.

You feel a searing pain as a bullet rips into your chest. You hear the sound of more gunfire, but you cannot tell who is shooting and who else is hit. You slump to the floor and head into the blackness of death.

» YOUR HASTY ACTION HAS COST YOUR LIFE.

Start the case again by going back to 1.

21

You nod. "I'll call Tucker."

You explain the situation to your boss, and that you need backup. "So who do you want?"

"We'll need Sun Lin for any forensic evidence we come up with. Blackwood can help give us an insight into The Cobra's mind."

"What about Bugs and Anusha?"

"We won't need Anusha," you say. "We know Smith died some hours ago. But I'll need Bugs."

"I'll get them on a military B-1 supersonic jet. They will be with you in less than four hours."

You ring off. Peters gestures towards the street. "I have a car waiting to take you to the airport, and a chartered plane to get you to London."

The small twin-engined plane takes off an hour later. The weather is bad all the way. Perez is nearly sick several times, much to your amusement!

Eventually the plane enters London airspace. It heads towards the City Airport. The River Thames is below. You look out of the plane's window and can just make out a series of strange-looking dome shapes, stretching across the river.

» **If you wish to ask the pilot about these, go to 43.**

» **If you don't want to bother him, go to 13.**

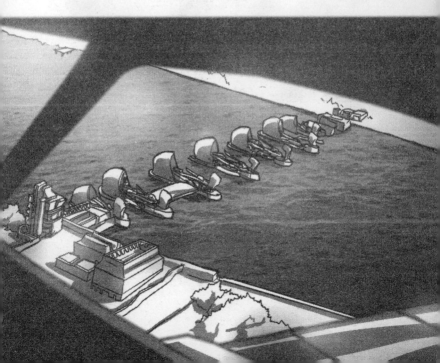

22

"It's the Bank of England!" you say. "That backs up the postcode that Agent Smith gave us. MI5 was right all along."

Todd looks at your piece of paper. "Boss, I think you've made a big mistake. Work it out again."

You soon realise that Todd is right.

» YOU MADE A BAD DECISION!

Make a note of this and go to 25.

23

"OK, let's get on with the case," you say. "We need to find The Cobra."

Sir James coughs. "Actually, I think we need to know more about what a 'dirty' bomb could do, don't you?"

"Why?" you ask.

"Because some potential targets would be more badly affected by a dirty bomb than others. If we know the intended target then we can hopefully track down The Cobra by predicting the moves he would have to make to get to it."

You have been too hasty. Sir James is right.

The head of MI5 looks at you as if you were a school kid. "Now, what do you know about 'dirty' bombs?"

» **YOU MADE A BAD DECISION!**

Make a note of this and go to 18.

24

"We'll follow MI5 to the Empire hotel," you tell the team. "It was a male driver and the hotel is near the intended target."

Todd shakes his head. "I think you're assuming too much," he says. "We don't know for sure that the bank is the target. Also didn't you tell me that The Cobra is a master of disguise?"

Perez nods. "And you said that in South America The Cobra escaped disguised as a woman."

You realise that the team are right and then you curse as you recall the picture of the woman driver. "The watch! The one the female driver was wearing – it was the one that Gomez had on when he was kidnapped. The Cobra must have taken it from him – the 'woman' in that car was The Cobra!"

Todd smiles. "He's made a mistake. That gives us a chance. We need to head to The Ritz."
"Shall we tell MI5?" asks Sun Lin.

YOU ALMOST MADE A MISTAKE, *BUT YOU GOT AWAY WITH IT!*

» **If you wish to inform MI5, go to 19.**
» **If you wish to head to the hotel without telling MI5, go to 38.**

25

You show the others the message:

Target Thames Barrier

"So it isn't the Bank of England," says Perez. "Why did Smith give us the bank's postcode before he died?"

You shrug. "It was just a red herring. It worked as well. It put us off the scent."

"What is this barrier?" asks Sin Lin.

» **If you asked the pilot about the barrier, go to 15.**

» **If you didn't ask the pilot, go to 35.**

26

"Sorry pal, you've got the wrong people," you tell the man.

"Really?" he replies. The man pulls out his phone, taps in a number and begins speaking quietly into it. With a smile he hands it to you.

A familiar voice shouts down the phone. "This is no time for messing about, you half-ass fool! You think I tell the whole world and his Auntie Mo where to find my goddam operatives?"

You grimace. It is your boss, Tucker. He continues to rant. "While you're sitting around, things are happening! Tell the man who you are and don't be such a…" Thankfully, the line goes dead.

You hand the phone back to the man and shrug.

» **YOU MADE A BAD DECISION!**
Make a note of this and go to 8.

27

"I'll catch up with him," you tell Bugs and open up the engines. You spot a speedboat on the river ahead of you – it must be The Cobra! Rain teems down as you close in on him. Ahead of you looms the Thames Barrier. It hasn't been raised yet.

You hear the thud of rotor blades get louder as a group of helicopters fly overhead. The Special Forces have arrived! You see The Cobra looking up. His boat speeds up. Your stomach churns as you see that he is heading straight for the barrier!

Frantically, you pull your gun out and start shooting. The Cobra returns fire. Gunfire erupts from the helicopters too – the Special Forces have also realised what The Cobra intends to do. Your heart pounds – bringing in the Special Forces was a bad mistake.

The Cobra's boat slams into one of the barrier's domes. There is a huge explosion. It is the last thing you see as the fireball rips through the air, engulfing you and your boat.

» **YOU HAVE FAILED AND PAID THE ULTIMATE PRICE.**
If you wish to begin again, go to 1.

28

Some time later you and the team meet up to
share the information you have pulled together.
You show people the Identikit picture you and
Todd have worked on.

"We'll get this out to every police officer in London," says Sir James.

You nod. "Good. But he will have changed his identity. He's a master of disguise." You turn to Bugs. "What have you got for us?"

"We've tracked all the cars that left the Guernsey to Portsmouth ferry. Only two of them came into London. Here are some pictures from CCTV along the route."

Bugs continues. "We've tracked them through London. Both drivers have gone to hotels. The male driver headed to the Empire hotel, near the Bank of England. The female driver has checked into The Ritz in Piccadilly."

Sir James nods. "It's obvious then, we send our men to the Empire." He turns to you. "Thank you for your help. We will take over now…"

You look at the pictures again. "But I think—"

Sir James interrupts you. "I appreciate your help, but this is now a Secret Service operation. We will sort it out from here."

» **If you're happy to let MI5 complete the operation, go to 44.**
» **If you have another plan, go to 12.**

29

You aim your gun.

"Cobra," you say. "I've got a gun pointed at you. Don't do anything stupid."

He turns slowly. "You again," he says. He points at the bomb. "I'm afraid you're too late. Like the last time…"

"Why are you doing this?" you ask. "Thousands could die… If it's just the money, then I'm sure the British Government will pay."

The Cobra nods his head. "Hmm, I like what you are proposing. How much would they offer?"

You lower your gun. "I'm sure that—"

You get no further. The Cobra throws himself at you with lightning speed. He knocks you backwards and your gun spins from your hand.

You look up. The Cobra is pointing a gun at you. "I don't negotiate," he says. "If I'm paid to do a job, I do it."

These are the last words you hear as he pulls the trigger…

» **THE COBRA HAS KILLED YOU.**

To start the case again, go to 1.

30

You signal to the team to move out and follow The Cobra. You all head towards the door.

However, at that moment, The Cobra doubles back into the hotel – he is checking to see if he was being followed. The team freezes and looks towards you. He follows their gaze and spots you.

The Cobra gives out a cry. "Crime Team!" He has recognised you!

In an instant he reaches for his gun. The team respond, but they are too slow. Cobra shoots, hitting Perez and Todd, who drop to the floor.

The lobby is full of screaming people as they take cover.

You pull out your gun and return fire, but you too are hit with a volley of bullets. You slump to the floor, blood pouring from a fatal wound.

» **YOU HAVE PAID FOR YOUR MISTAKE WITH YOUR LIFE.**
Start the case again by going back to 1.

31

You tap at the keyboard and enter the code.

You stare at the countdown. It doesn't stop! You have put in the wrong code. You try to change it, but there is a flash of light, a deafening boom and your world goes black…

» **YOU HAVE PAID THE ULTIMATE PRICE.**
If you wish to begin again, go to 1.

32

You say the words out loud. "E see two r ate ay a ch... what's that supposed to mean?"

"The person who took the message had to guess what your man Smith was saying as he was dying. Smith wasn't speaking too clearly," says Perez. "What if he wasn't trying to say words, but letters and numbers instead? Remember the postcode the driver punched into the sat nav?" Perez sounds the words of the message out slowly. "Easy too are – could that be 'E – C – 2 – R'?"

"Perez," you say, "you're a genius."

"I'll remind you of that at my next pay review – how does the rest of it go?"

You check the transcript. "Ate ay a ch."

"Ate ay a ch…" Perez narrows his eyes in thought. "Could be 8 – A – H?"

Sir James slaps his hand on the table. "E C 2 R 8 A H! Brilliant!"

"What's at that postcode?" you ask.

"Check the location," Sir James tells one of his people.

"It's the Bank of England, sir."

"That's right in the heart of London's financial centre," says Sir James.

"Now that would be a heck of a target," you say. "Without the bank, there'd be a financial crisis."

At that moment the door opens and the other members of Crime Team walk in.

"Glad you could join us," says Perez. "What took you so long?"

"I need to speak to my boss," you tell Sir James.

He nods. "We've already set up a comms link." He presses buttons on a remote control and Tucker's face appears on a huge wall monitor.

"What's going on?" he asks.

You quickly bring Tucker and the rest of the Crime Team up to speed with the case so far.

"So what are your plans now?" asks Tucker.

» **If you want to go to the Bank of England and stake it out, go to 2.**

» **If you think you should try to track down The Cobra, go to 14.**

33

"Keep looking for him," you tell Perez.

"But it's a waste of time," says Leon. "We should get back to see what Bugs has found."

You glare at him. "Just do it!"

Perez shrugs and heads into the Underground station. You too push through the crowds, trying to spot The Cobra. But it is hopeless. He has given you the slip.

Some time later, Perez meets up with you. "Nothing, boss. We've lost him and wasted valuable time."

You realise that Perez is right.

» **YOU MADE A BAD DECISION.**

Make a note of it and go to 11.

34

"No time," you say. "Wait here. I need to meet the agent I told you about."

Perez shakes his head. "Bad move, chief. What if you're walking into a trap? If I don't know where you're going or who you're seeing and why, how can I provide backup? I don't want to have to report to Tucker and tell him you got your head busted and I don't have any leads because you didn't tell me anything…"

You realise that he is right. Perez needs to know

everything. And the last thing you need is Tucker on your back!

» **YOU MADE A MISTAKE,** *BUT HAVE GOT AWAY WITH IT!*
  Go to 42.

35

"We need to find out about this barrier," you say. "Bugs, get us some info."

Bugs taps at the computer.

> The Thames Barrier is a flood control system. It consists of ten gates that can be raised and lowered. It protects London from flooding caused by high tides. It is raised during very high tides and storm surges.
>
> It protects over 125sq km of land, over a million people, billions of pounds of property including hospitals, power stations, historic buildings and parts of the London underground train network. If it were to fail, London would be devastated.

"Check the weather reports and see if the barrier is going to be raised in the near future," you tell Bugs.

Minutes later he has the information. "High tides, storm weather due – high risk of flooding. The barrier is going to be raised in the next hour."

"It's the perfect target," you whisper. "If the control room that operates the barrier was blown up with a dirty bomb, the barrier wouldn't rise and the water would flood London. The damage would be colossal."

At that moment your phone rings. It is Tucker. You tell him what you have discovered.

"Then why haven't you told MI5?"

"We've only just found out about the barrier, boss," you reply, wishing you'd asked the pilot about the barrier on your way into London.

"You're supposed to know these things," he yells. "Information is important! Always gather facts, 'cos if you don't there won't be a job for you at Crime Team. And that's a warning! I'll let MI5 know what is happening. You can get your sorry backsides to the barrier, NOW!"

» **YOU'VE RECEIVED A WARNING FROM TUCKER!**
Make a note of this and go to 9.

36

You tap at the keyboard and enter the code.

Desperately you stare at the countdown as it ticks down…

00.05
00.04
00.03

You brace yourself for the explosion, but then the countdown stops! You breathe a sigh of relief – your guess was right.

There is a clatter of noise from the doorway. You turn to see several members of the Special Forces charging into the room.

You hold up your hands. "You're a little late… It's all been taken care of!"

» **Go to 45.**

37

"Call off the Special Forces," you tell Bugs. "If The Cobra sees them, he'll know we're on to him and could detonate the bomb. Tell them to head to the barrier, but keep hidden. I'll follow him."

You keep your boat back at a safe distance. Some minutes later, the Thames Barrier comes into view. You see the Cobra steer his boat to a jetty and head up a flight of steps to a control tower. He is carrying a large aluminium case. You let him go into the building before bringing your boat alongside the jetty.

There is no sign of the Special Forces or MI5 officers. You realise that you are on your own against The Cobra.

You make your way to the control building. You see the body of a security guard lying in the doorway. You bend down to check his pulse, but he is dead. The Cobra is ruthless and you know he will spare no one.

You take out your gun and slowly enter the building.

In the dim light you see The Cobra ahead of you. He is bending over the case. You can see green and red lights flashing from inside. He has not seen you.

» **If you want to take this opportunity to take him out, go to 5.**
» **If you choose to negotiate with him, go to 29.**

38

"OK, we'll head to The Ritz without telling the Brits. MI5 wanted us off the case," you say, "nuts to them."

"Ritz and Brits… sheer poetry," murmurs Perez.

You stare at him. He shuts up and you continue. "If Cobra has the bomb, we need to go in gently."

You flag down a taxicab and are soon at The Ritz Hotel. Bugs and Sun Lin settle down in the lobby to keep an eye on the entrance. Bugs opens up his laptop computer while you, Todd and Perez head to the desk and ask for the manager. You explain who you are and he agrees to work with you.

Soon you have the information you need. The "woman" checked into room 101 on the first floor. You ask to see the CCTV footage from the floor.

As you are watching, a figure emerges from room 101. You recognise him at once. It is The Cobra!

What should you do?

» **If you want to call in the Secret Service, go to 3.**

» **If you want to take The Cobra out yourself, go to 20.**

» **If you want to follow The Cobra, go to 7.**

39

"OK," you say. "We need to head to London. If The Cobra is there we need to follow him."

Peters nods. "Our people in London will tell you all about the operation when we get there. We have a plane waiting for you."

You look outside at the stormy weather.

"Flying in this?" you say.

"It's the only way," replies Peters. "All sea travel to the UK mainland has been cancelled in the last hour."

"I hope you've got plenty of paper bags for the trip," you mutter.

"What about getting some backup?" Perez asks you.

» **If you want to call for Crime Team backup, go to 21.**
» **If you think that you and Perez can deal with the situation, go to 4.**

40

"We head to The Ritz," you tell the others.

Perez looks at you open mouthed. "We're looking for a male. A male driver of a car that came off the Guernsey ferry checked into a hotel near the Bank of England, which is the target. What am I missing?"

"The obvious," you reply. "We don't know for sure that the Bank of England is the target. The Cobra is a master of disguise. Remember that in South America he escaped disguised as a woman."

"Good thinking, boss," says Todd.

"There was also something nagging at my mind. The watch that the woman driver was wearing – it's the same one that The Cobra was wearing when I met him. It's the one that Gomez was wearing when he was kidnapped. The Cobra must have taken it from him. The Cobra was disguised as the female driver! He is at The Ritz!"

Todd smiles. "He's made a mistake. That gives us a chance. Shall we tell MI5?"

» If you wish to inform MI5, go to 19.
» If you wish to head to The Ritz Hotel without telling MI5, go to 38.

You show the others what you have written:

"So what?" asks Perez.

"You take the top letter, then look at its number: line them up and see what letter it stands for. C1 is 'A', B3 is 'M' and so on."

"Nice one, boss," says Sun Lin.

You begin to work out the message.

You finish and look up. "We know the target!"

» **If you think the target is the Bank of England, go to 22.**

» **If you think the target is something else, go to 25.**

"It started when you were on holiday," you say. "We received this request." You pass a document to Perez.

HIGHEST SECURITY

CRIME: KIDNAPPING

NAME: HUGO GOMEZ

JOB: CHIEF EXECUTIVE OF BLACK
           OIL INTERNATIONAL

Kidnapped in Caracas, Venezuela,
by unknown persons.

Ransom Demand of $10 Million

REQUEST CRIME TEAM DEAL WITH
NEGOTIATIONS AND PAYMENT OF RANSOM

"I went to Venezuela with Sun Lin and Todd to deal with the situation," you explain. "Gomez was a top man and his company had no hesitation in paying the ransom. We did some digging around and discovered that it was The Cobra behind the kidnapping."

"So he's a kidnapper too?" says Perez.

"He'll do anything if the money is right… Anyway, to cut a long story short, I delivered the money directly to him. I insisted on a face-to-face meeting. He agreed."

"Unbelievable!" Perez whistles. "You met him?

You must be one of the only people in the world who knows what he looks like! What happened?"

"We set up an ambush, but he got away with the money. He disguised himself as a woman!"

"Nice," nods Perez. "Did you get Gomez back?"

You scowl. "No. We found his body. He'd been killed days before. The Cobra never intended to keep him alive. He's untrustworthy and ruthless."

"So what are we doing here?"

"I've traced some of the ransom money to a bank in Guernsey – we're supposed to be meeting an intelligence officer from the British Secret Service."

"Who is it, James Bond?" laughs Perez.

You smile. "He's called Smith. At least that's what he told me. He's been trying to infiltrate The Cobra's circle of contacts. He was the person who put me onto the money… He's going to meet us and take us to the bank where the ransom money ended up."

At that moment the door opens and a man enters. He walks straight up to you. "Tucker sent me," he says. "I take it you are Crime Team?"

You look at him – you've never seen this person before…

» **If you want to say yes, go to 8.**
» **If you want to say no, go to 26.**

43

"What's that stretching across the river?" you ask the pilot.

"The Thames Barrier," he replies. "It protects London from high tides and storm surges. It is raised if there is the possibility of flooding. It stops the water from heading into the city and causing devastation. They say that if the Thames flooded, thousands of buildings in London would be destroyed, power supplies would go down and over a million people would be affected. Business would grind to a halt and the Underground train system would be out of action for years."

"Incredible," you murmur. You look out at the pouring rain. "Will this weather cause it to close?"

The pilot laughs. "It's a safe bet that it will, but at the moment I'm more concerned with the air up here, not the water down there! Hold on tight. We're coming in to land."

» Go to 13.

44

"If that's the way you want it, fine!" you snap. "Come on team, we're leaving."

Bugs and Todd protest. "We've just flown halfway round the world for this."

"The man says leave it to him, so let's do just

that." You leave Thames House and head for the airport. As you sit in the departure lounge you get a call from Tucker.

"We've just had reports that The Cobra has got away! The Brits went to the wrong hotel! I thought you were supposed to be helping out!"

"They didn't want our help," you say.

"You should have insisted!"

"OK," you say, "we'll head back to MI5."

"Don't bother!" yells Tucker. "I don't need some sulky weakling leading my team. Get your sorry butt back here and clear your desk – you're out!"

» **YOU'VE BEEN THROWN OFF THE TEAM!**

To see how you rate as a detective, go to 46.

45

A couple of days later, you and the team arrive back in your office. Tucker is waiting for you. "Well done," he says.

Wow! I'm getting praise from Tucker, you think. What is the world coming to?

Then the world returns to normal. "But Sir James wasn't happy that you didn't give MI5 all the information you gathered. Not happy at all."

"We saved London from disaster," you protest, "there's no pleasing some people!"

Tucker shakes his head. "You took a big risk, doing it all on your own."

"Hey, boss," says Perez. "That's why you employ us – we're the best!"

You nod. "Absolutely! We saved London and got rid of a ruthless international mercenary."

Tucker nods. "OK, not a bad day's work, I suppose. Just don't get too big headed – there's always going to be another case for Crime Team!"

» **You've cracked the case – well done!**
Go to 46 to see how you rate as a detective...

46

How do you rate as a
Crime Team detective?

WASHOUT – if you were THROWN OFF THE CASE
or were THROWN OUT OF THE TEAM.
Polish up your detective skills and go back to 1.

AMATEUR – at least ONE WARNING.
You need to try harder. See if you can do better on
other CRIME TEAM cases.

⭐ **ONE-STAR AGENT –** no warnings, but made THREE
or more BAD DECISIONS.
You need to boost your detecting skills. See if you can
stay more alert on other CRIME TEAM cases.

⭐ ⭐ **TWO-STAR AGENT –** no warnings, but made TWO
BAD DECISIONS.
Maybe you're lacking in confidence. Try looking for less
help on other CRIME TEAM cases.

⭐ ⭐ ⭐ **THREE-STAR AGENT –** no warnings, but made
ONE BAD DECISION.
You're a worthy leader of CRIME TEAM – well done!
But can you do as well on other CRIME TEAM cases?

 FIRST-CLASS CRIME TEAM AGENT – no warnings,
and made no bad decisions.
You're a genius detective! Bet you can't do as well on
other CRIME TEAM cases…